BIG HOPE

WRITTEN BY SANDY SILVERTHORNE

ILLUSTRATED BY DANIEL HAWKINS

HARVEST HOUSE PUBLISHERS

EUGENE, OREGON

Cover design by Dugan Design Group

HARVEST KIDS is a trademark of The Hawkins Children's LLC. Harvest House Publishers, Inc., is the exclusive licensee of the trademark HARVEST KIDS.

Big Hope
Copyright © 2019 by Sandy Silverthorne
Artwork © 2019 by Daniel Hawkins
Published by Harvest House Publishers
Eugene, Oregon 97408
www.harvesthousepublishers.com

ISBN 978-0-7369-7707-4 (pbk.) (The 1687 Foundation edition)

Printed in the United States of America

20 21 22 23 24 25 26 27 / CM-CD / 10 9 8 7 6 5 4 3 2

This book has been made available without charge by The 1687 Foundation, a nonprofit, tax-exempt organization dedicated to advancing Christian and charitable purposes. Please note that this book may only be given away as a free gift. It may not be sold, used as an encouragement for any charitable gifts, or provided for any commercial or personal-gain purpose whatsoever.

For additional information, please contact The 1687 Foundation at
www.1687foundation.com
Tel: 541.549.7600   Fax: 541.549.7603

INTRODUCTION

You're about to enter an awesome adventure! You're going to witness—and **COLOR**—God creating the universe from nothing. You'll catch a glimpse of Noah building his ark, God opening the Red Sea, and Jesus calming the storm. And you'll see how Jesus's sacrifice opens the way for us to be friends with God. So let's get started! You can color these pages with crayons, colored pencils, or even markers. Pretty soon you're going to have a book filled with your own beautiful masterpieces!

CONTENTS

CREATION

The earth was empty and without form. But then God spoke.

Let there be **LIGHT**!

On the second day, God spoke again, and the heavens were created and separated from the earth.

Then God spoke again...

Let the waters be divided, and let the dry land appear.

And let the earth be covered with grass, herbs, and fruit trees.

And suddenly, at God's command, trees and vines full of sweet, delicious fruit sprang up all over the earth.

The next day God spoke again, and the air above the water was suddenly filled with birds of every kind.

And under the sea, thousands of kinds of fish appeared!

And then on the seventh day, God looked around, very pleased with His new creation, and announced that it was **VERY GOOD.** Then He rested from all of His work.

They worked every day building the ark, even as the people made fun of them.

God told Noah to gather a male and female of every kind of animal to take on the ark with him.

They also brought food and supplies for themselves and all the animals.

Bring every sort of food...

and don't leave out the healthy kinds!

Then, just as Noah turned 600, they heard the rumble of thunder in the distance. It was time to go into the ark. The rain had begun to pour.

BA-BOOM

Noah, his family, and all the animals got on board.

And once they were inside, God closed the door.

SLAM!

Noah, his family, and all of the animals came down out of the ark, ready to begin a new life!

GROWING UP MOSES

"My Presence will go with you, and I will give you rest."
– Exodus 33:14 –

When the baby Moses was born, an evil king ruled over Egypt. He feared and hated God's people so much that he ordered that all male Hebrew babies should be killed.

But Moses's mother hid her newborn son.

She made a little boat, placed him inside, and set him in the river.

His big sister watched over him from the river banks.

After Moses had drifted for a while, the daughter of the king found him. As soon as she saw Moses, she loved him and took him to be her son.

So Moses was raised in the king's palace. He was taught to read, write, and be a leader. He became a prince—a prince of Egypt.

But many years later, Moses left Egypt and became a shepherd in the desert.

One day while he was up on a very high mountain, he saw an amazing thing—a bush that was on fire but not burning up!

Moses...

God spoke to Moses from within the bush.

THE PLAGUES

So Moses returned to Egypt and pleaded with the king—Pharaoh—to let the Hebrew people go. But the king refused. So God sent plagues on the land to convince Pharaoh to let God's people leave the land of Egypt.

God turned the Nile River into blood.

He sent millions of frogs all over the land. They were everywhere!

Then clouds of gnats swarmed all of Egypt and its people.

Then millions of flies invaded the land!

After that, all the livestock of Egypt got sick.

"By this you will know that I am the LORD."
- Exodus 7:17 -

And the Egyptian people got painful sores on their skin! Only God's people were spared.

OW!

Then from out of the sky came a huge hailstorm! The hail was mixed with fire!

After the hail, locusts came and ate the crops that remained!

Then God sent darkness over all the land!

But the king still wouldn't agree to let Moses take his people out of Egypt. So God allowed the firstborn child of all the Egyptian people to die. This was the worst plague of all.

EXODUS AND THE RED SEA

"Don't be afraid. Just stand where you are and watch, and you will see the wonderful way the Lord will rescue you today."
— Exodus 14:13 TLB —

Even Pharaoh's son died from the last plague. Finally Pharaoh had had enough.

All the children of Israel followed Moses as he led them out of Egypt.

So the Israelites hurried into the sea, crossing over to the other side without so much as getting damp. All night long, they walked over on dry land. It was God's miraculous deliverance!

When Moses and the people realized that God had saved them from their enemies, they rejoiced and worshiped the Lord right there on the seashore. God had come to their rescue!

DAVID AND GOLIATH

Being the youngest in his family, David was asked to run an errand for his father.

So David left his father in Bethlehem and went to the Valley of Elah.

Take these loaves and cheese to your brothers on the battlefield.

When David arrived at the camp of the Israelites, he heard shouting from the valley below.

YOO-HOO! HEEE-BREWS!

GOD VISITS THE WORLD

"For there is born to you this day in the city of David a Savior, who is Christ the Lord."
- Luke 2:11 NKJV -

On a cold night in Bethlehem in Israel, Mary and Joseph, a young couple expecting their first child, wandered into town. They'd been forced to travel to the small village in order to be counted for the Roman census.

INN
NO VACANCY

As they went from house to house and inn to inn, they discovered there was not a bed to be found. A kind innkeeper felt bad for them and allowed them to spend the night in his stable.

There, among the sheep, cows, and donkeys, their baby, Jesus, was born. But this was no ordinary baby. It was God Himself, wrapped in swaddling clothes. He'd become a man—a baby, actually—in order to visit His creation and make a way for people to know Him.

The angels rejoiced, and shepherds and wise men came to visit this very special child. They'd come to worship the newborn King.

LET THE LITTLE CHILDREN COME

"Let the little children come to me."
– Mark 10:14 –

Everywhere Jesus went, large crowds followed Him. One day, some moms and dads brought their children to Jesus so He could bless them.

THROUGH THE ROOF

"For I am the LORD, who heals you."
– Exodus 15:26 –

A huge crowd began to gather around a little house in Capernaum.

Jesus was inside, teaching about God's love. So many people had come to hear Him speak, there wasn't room for anyone else in the house.

47

So they picked up their friend on his mat and started running to the house where Jesus was teaching.

But when they turned the corner, their hearts sank. There were so many people crowded around the house, there was no way they could get inside, much less reach Jesus.

The **ROOF!**

But then one of them got an idea.

Son, everything you've ever done wrong has been forgiven.

Who is this man who thinks He can even forgive people?

Only God can do that!

Jesus knew what they were thinking.

To show that I have the power to forgive people...

Get up. Pick up your mat and go home.

With that, the boy jumped up, picked up his mat, and walked out of the house! He was healed!

We've never seen anything like this!

53

Jesus spent the whole day on the hillside, teaching the people about God and how much He loved them.

Who is this man who can even control the wind?

Even the storms obey Him!

Perhaps their thoughts returned to Psalm 107:29, written centuries before: "God will calm the storm and still the waves."

Your faith is too small.

Don't be afraid, just believe.

GOD'S GREATEST GIFT

"I am the resurrection and the life."
– John 11:25 –

Just as the Passover was beginning, the priests and leaders of the people came and took Jesus. They tied Him up and led Him to Pilate, the Roman ruler of the city.

I find nothing wrong with this Man. Why don't I release Him to you?

NO! GIVE US BARABBAS!!

(Barabbas was a rebel and a murderer.)

So Pilate agreed.

Jesus was whipped, beaten, and spit upon. He was forced to carry His cross through the crowded streets of Jerusalem and up the hill to Golgotha.

Two followers of Jesus—Joseph of Arimathea and Nicodemus—came, took Jesus's body from the cross, and placed Him in Joseph's family tomb. It was a brand-new tomb that had never been used. They placed Jesus's lifeless body inside and rolled a stone over the opening to seal it.

Three days later, some of the women who followed Jesus showed up at the tomb. But what they found shocked them!

Later, Jesus appeared to the disciples, in the upper room, along the road, by the seashore, and even to **FIVE HUNDRED** people at once!

By rising from the dead and living forever, Jesus proved He really is who He said He was—God's Son. If we believe in Him and receive the gift of His sacrifice on the cross for all the wrong things we've done, we can start a friendship with Him and live with Him forever.

OFFERING FREE RESOURCES
OF *hope & encouragement*

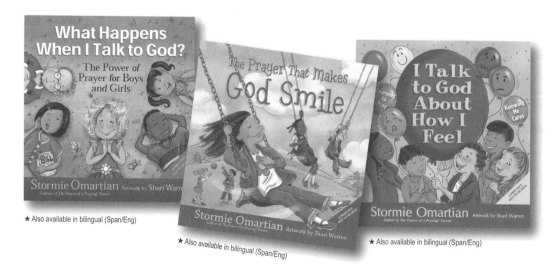

★ Also available in bilingual (Span/Eng)

★ Also available in bilingual (Span/Eng)

★ Also available in bilingual (Span/Eng)

Contact us for additional information:

TEL: 541.549.7600 FAX: 541.549.7603

www.1687foundation.com

P.O. Box 1961, Sisters, OR 97759